THE EXPLORER'S LIBRARY

Edited Selections from the Works of

Dr MONTY FITZGIBBON BSc (VET)

TYRANNOSAUR

AND OTHER CARNIVOROUS BIPEDAL DINOSAURS
OF NORTH AMERICA

ILLUSTRATED PLATES
by eminent Artist & Printmaker DIZ WALLIS

EDITORIAL
by Consultant & Writer CLINT TWIST

SKETCHES IN THE FIELD BY EMMA NICHOLLS

PUBLISHED IN THE UNITED KINGDOM BY TEMPLAR PUBLISHING

PREHISTORIC MONSTER FOUND IN MONTANA

NEWFOUNDLAND MONTHLY MESSENGER — FEBRUARY 1903

AN expedition sent by the American Museum of Natural History last year discovered the bones of a gigantic meat-eating dinosaur in eastern Montana. The expedition was organised and led by experienced fossil-hunter Barnum Brown. The new dinosaur was described as having a six-foot skull with dozens of teeth the size of table knives. When questioned by a reporter,

Mr Brown stated that it would take several seasons of hard work to excavate all the bones. They will be freighted back to New York so that palaeontologist Henry Osborn can study them. Mr Osborn, who is well known in scientific circles, has been in charge of the museum's Department of Vertebrate Palaeontology since 1897.

16th March 1907
Garrison Headquarters,
St John's, Newfoundland

Mr Barnum Brown
c/o American Museum
of Natural History
New York City

Dear Mr Brown,

Please excuse this uninvited communication from a stranger in a distant place. I have read with great interest a newspaper report concerning your recent discovery of a carnivorous dinosaur, and I have become quite obsessed by this prehistoric beast.

Mine is not merely an idle interest. I am a qualified veterinarian, fully trained in vertebrate anatomy. Dinosaurs have fascinated me since I was a boy, and I scarcely dared dream that I might one day see their fossilised remains for myself.

Through fortunate circumstance, I have the opportunity to take a leave of absence from my duties (which largely consist of tending to my fellow officers' horses). I am no stranger to the rigours of travel, and I can bring my own provisions.

Would you be kind enough to consider permitting an enthusiastic amateur to visit your excavations, in order that he may see for himself some dinosaur bones?

I am sir, yours sincerely,

Mouby.

J. E. M. Fitzgibbon,
Captain (Acting), Army Veterinary Corps

DEPARTMENT OF VERTEBRATE PALAEONTOLOGY,
American Museum of Natural History
NEW YORK, NY, USA

November 27, 1907

Dear Mr Fitzgibbon,

I have received your letter dated March 16th 1907.

When my excavations are completed, the reconstructed skeleton will be displayed to the public here in New York. If you are impatient with this prospect, I have no objection in principle to your visiting Montana.

We shall be in the vicinity of Hell Creek, a day's ride north of Miles City, for most of next summer. If you are successful in locating our camp, I shall endeavour to make you welcome. Perhaps your professional skills may be of some benefit to our mules.

Kindly do not wear your uniform, nor expect me to acknowledge your military rank. This museum is an entirely civilian establishment.

Yours,

P.P.

(Dictated by Mr Brown and signed in his absence.)

CONTENTS

THE ADVENTURE BEGINS	4-5
UNEARTHING THE BEAST	6-7
THE MIGHTY TYRANNOSAURUS	8-9
ALLOSAURUS AND CERATOSAURUS	10-11
THOUGHTS AND IDEAS	12-13
ANCIENT CALAMITY	14-15
THE TERRIBLE CLAW	16-17
A PREHISTORIC CONNECTION	18-19
A PREDATOR IN PURSUIT	20-21
A FAMILY TREE	22-23

ABOUT THE AUTHOR

MONTY FITZGIBBON & THE TRAIL OF BARNUM BROWN

ABOUT MONTY – OUR AMATEUR HERO

James Edward Montgomery Fitzgibbon, 'Monty', was born in Scotland in 1879, the only child of an Aberdeen fish merchant. He attended the local school, and later studied Veterinary Medicine at university in England. After receiving his degree in June 1902, he joined the Army rather than return to Scotland. He was immediately posted to Newfoundland, and arrived there in November 1902.

There is very little information about the following years – his distinctly unmilitary scrawl 'Monty' is to be found on very few documents. He made little impression upon the army until his sudden departure. Lieutenant Fitzgibbon was officially declared missing in September 1908.

His book – which Templar Publishing here reprint from the only existing copy – sheds considerable light on his adventures during that unauthorised absence. Monty became utterly obsessed with dinosaur fossils and continued his researches around the American Rockies long after Barnum Brown had departed for other locations. This extraordinary volume, filled with his sense of excitement and wonder, is also remarkable for being one of the very first attempts to provide a comprehensive view of carnivorous dinosaurs.

ABOUT BARNUM BROWN – THE INSPIRATION

Barnum Brown is one of the most celebrated names in American palaeontology (the study of fossils). Born in Kansas in 1873 (he was named after a great showman, P. T. Barnum, whose travelling circus had visited the state), he became interested in fossils while at college. In 1897 he was hired by Henry Osborn to join the staff of the American Museum. Although the discovery of *Tyrannosaurus* in 1902 was probably the most important event of his long career, Brown continued fossil hunting for a further 60 years. In addition to his discoveries in the USA and Canada, Brown also travelled to Mexico, India and Pakistan. He died in 1963, a few days short of his 90th birthday.

MONTY FITZGIBBON
VETERINARIAN AND EXPLORER
BORN IN SCOTLAND 1879

BARNUM BROWN
PALAEONTOLOGIST
BORN IN KANSAS 1873

* *April 1908 - the journey begins…*

I set off on my new adventure aboard a steamer bound for New York with no expectation that my journey would become so extended – or indeed that it would be so fascinating. My intention was first to visit Montana to find Mr Barnum Brown's camp, but to stay for only a couple of weeks at most. Hopeful that my role at Barnum's dinosaur dig would be more than that of onlooker, I tried my best to help and ask questions whenever possible. My desire to contribute did not go unnoticed, and Barnum always treated me with the greatest kindness, patiently answering my multitude of questions and making quite sure that I properly understood his answers.

At that time, I had no idea that I possessed 'an exceptional eye' for spotting fossils, or that I could so easily learn to 'read' the rocks. These talents might have remained completely unknown and unused if they had not been identified by Barnum himself and developed under his expert guidance. If this journal – my own modest contribution to the study of these ancient beasts – has any value at all, it is because I had the best of all possible teachers.

*EDITOR'S FOOTNOTE
This introduction was attached to Monty's journal marked 'dedicatory preface'.

A MAP OF MY NORTH AMERICAN JOURNEY

Key:

┼┼┼┼┼┼ Railway

╌ ╌ ╌ ╌ Route Taken

1. *Miles City and the* T. rex *site*
2. *My encounter with a bear*
3. Deinonychus *discovery*
4. Allosaurus *quarry*
5. *Grand Canyon*
5a. *Monument Valley*
6. Coelophysis
7. *Texas - a footprint trail*
8. *Dallas*
9. *Galveston*

UNITED STATES

BY J. BARTHOLOMEW F.R.G.S.

British Miles

Kilometres

EDITOR'S NOTES
INFORMATION TO EQUIP THE READER

In 1913, the general public knew very little about science and dinosaurs. Monty Fitzgibbon wanted to place the following explanatory paragraphs at the beginning of his book. The age of the Earth was then estimated at about 100 million years. We now know the Earth to be about 4.6 billion years old. The Triassic, Jurassic and Cretaceous periods had a combined length of some 180 million years. Dinosaurs walked the Earth for many millions of years, until some 65 million years ago, when they became extinct.

IMPORTANCE OF ROCK LAYERS

The Earth's surface consists of layers of rock laid one upon the other, formed either by the outpourings of lava from volcanoes, or from sediments washed into rivers and seas. The oldest rocks are found at the greatest depth, with progressively younger rocks lying above them. Geologists (Earth scientists) have grouped these layers, called strata, into a series of named time periods, each of which lasted for more than a million years. This book is concerned with fossils found in rocks from the Triassic, Jurassic and Cretaceous periods. These three periods are sometimes grouped together as the so-called Age of Reptiles.

CONCERNING FOSSILS

Fossils are the preserved remains of ancient animals. When an animal dies, its body may become buried beneath layers of mud or sand. In this state, certain parts of the animal (such as its bones, teeth or shell) may be preserved by gradually being transformed into stone – a process scientists call petrification. With more layers of mud and rock being deposited above, the petrified remains are hidden for millions of years until they are revealed, either through natural events or excavation.

ON THE NATURE OF DINOSAURS

The dinosaurs were a group of reptiles, generally of immense size. Their reptilian nature can be seen from their skull bones, which look like those of some living reptiles. Dinosaurs were first identified from fossils in 1841, and their study has since made remarkable progress. We know from their teeth that most dinosaurs, including the very largest, were plant-eaters like elephants. Others had long sharp teeth and were evidently meat-eaters.

CHAPTER I.

THE ADVENTURE BEGINS

IN WHICH I TRAVEL FAR TO BEGIN MY NEW LIFE AS A FOSSIL HUNTER

Brief enquiries in New York having established that Brown was indeed in Montana, I bought a ticket on the first train heading for the West. From Chicago, located on the flat, windswept shores of Lake Michigan, I travelled on a train bound for Seattle via St Pierre. It was as we chugged across the Great Plains that I noticed my surroundings were gradually becoming more arid. I was still pondering the reasons for this – perhaps the rain that is so common near the coast does not reach this far inland – when I caught my first sight of the rugged mountains that were to become my second home, the magnificent Rockies! Miles City is not a very big town, but I was able to equip myself with a good horse and some basic supplies. I also managed to locate Barnum's expedition without any undue difficulty, by means of a very simple plan. I waited near the railroad stop until one of their wagons arrived loaded with bones for shipment to New York. When the wagon returned to their encampment, I just trailed along.

THE GREAT NORTHERN RAILROAD
MY WESTWARD JOURNEY WAS GREATLY FACILITATED BY THIS 'IRON HORSE' WHICH RIDES THE MOST NORTHERLY OF THE SIX TRANSCONTINENTAL RAIL ROUTES THAT ARE AVAILABLE TO THE AMERICAN TRAVELLING PUBLIC.

ROCK TYPES

I soon learned to recognise and ignore volcanic rocks and those that have been affected by volcanic heat. Amateur fossil-hunters must soon learn that these kinds of rock very rarely contain fossils. It is the sedimentary rocks, such as sandstone, mudstone and limestone, that are the great storehouses of the fossil record and therefore the best hunting grounds for true dinosaur enthusiasts.

Most sedimentary rocks were laid down beneath the saltwater of oceans and seas. These marine sediments (as such rocks are known among geologists) may contain large numbers of fossil shellfish and the like; or they may be entirely devoid of fossils. In either case they are of little interest to the student of land-living dinosaurs. It is freshwater sediments, laid down by rivers, ponds and lakes, that are most likely to contain dinosaur fossils. To my good fortune, it is precisely these types of rock that are so abundantly exposed to sight in the regions of the Rocky Mountains.

FINDING FOSSILS

It is no coincidence that my researches into fossil dinosaurs took place in the rainless shadows of the Rocky Mountains - fossils are simply most often found in rock. In the more hospitable parts of the world, the fossil-bearing rock is usually hidden from sight by layers of soil and vegetation. However, in the drier regions around the Rocky Mountains, the rock is easier to see. To put it another way - there are endless empty miles of nothing but bare rock! Among these barren wastes, a keen eye may occasionally be rewarded with sight of a fossil. Something catches the attention; it may be sunlight glinting on a fragment of petrified bone, or a shape that stands out from the others, or even a subtle change in the colour or texture of the rock itself. Only careful inspection will reveal whether it is indeed a fossil - and 99 times out of every 100 it is not.

THIS SKETCH OF CRATED BONES AT THE RAIL DEPOT AWAITING SHIPMENT NEATLY CAPTURES THE HUSTLE AND BUSTLE OF LIFE IN MILES CITY.

CHAPTER II.

UNEARTHING THE BEAST

IN WHICH I FIND THAT EXCAVATING FOSSILS REQUIRES BOTH MENTAL DILIGENCE AND PHYSICAL LABOUR

My first days in Montana were spent in smiling bewilderment as I wandered around and watched the expedition team go about its work with practised skill. It was immediately apparent that, compared to myself, even the teamsters who drove the wagon were veritable experts on the subject of dinosaur fossils. Fortunately, I could recall sufficient detail concerning the anatomy of reptiles so as not to appear a complete ignoramus. To be honest, I found the fragmented nature of the bones extremely difficult to comprehend, and it was only much later that I was able to make any sense of the skeleton.

BARNUM BROWN IN THE FIELD

ON A ROCK-STREWN MONTANA HILLSIDE, BARNUM BROWN (WEARING HAT, AT LEFT) EXAMINES A FRAGMENTED DINOSAUR BONE THAT IS STILL IN THE PROCESS OF BEING UNCOVERED.

has convinced Mr Brown that the dinosaurs must have died close to an ancient river, so that their bones became buried in sand when the river flooded. They had previously recovered the beast's hind limbs and tail from another fossil specimen in similar rock some miles distant.

FIELD WORK

The sandstone is extremely hard, and difficult to work with hand tools. Fortunately, it is not necessary to remove every trace of the surrounding rock from the fossils. That painstaking task, I was informed, is left to the experts in the museum laboratories. The job of the field-men (I count myself an honorary member of this intrepid team) is to uncover the fossil, and then divide it into slabs that are small enough to be lifted onto a wagon and taken to the rail depot.

FIRST CLUES

I soon learned that the expedition had found several incomplete specimens of the dinosaur at different locations. The specimen being excavated in the summer of 1908 was discovered when a member of the party noticed four vertebrae exposed by weathering on a sandstone ridge. Beneath the dirt and rock were many more vertebrae, together with the pelvis. The skull, which had become detached from the neck bones, lay nearby. The nature of the sandstone

DANGER, DYNAMITE!

Our task of uncovering and dividing the fossil was made easier by using dynamite. Great care must be taken when using explosives for such a delicate operation, and it requires considerable experience to estimate the right amount. If the explosive charge is too small, there will be no great effect; but if the charge is too big, then the bones will be pulverised into worthless powder by the force of the explosion.

THE MOST GRIEVOUS PERIL FACED BY THE PRECIOUS CARGO OF FOSSILS WAS BEING BUMPED AND SHAKEN TO PIECES ON THE WAGON TO MILES CITY.

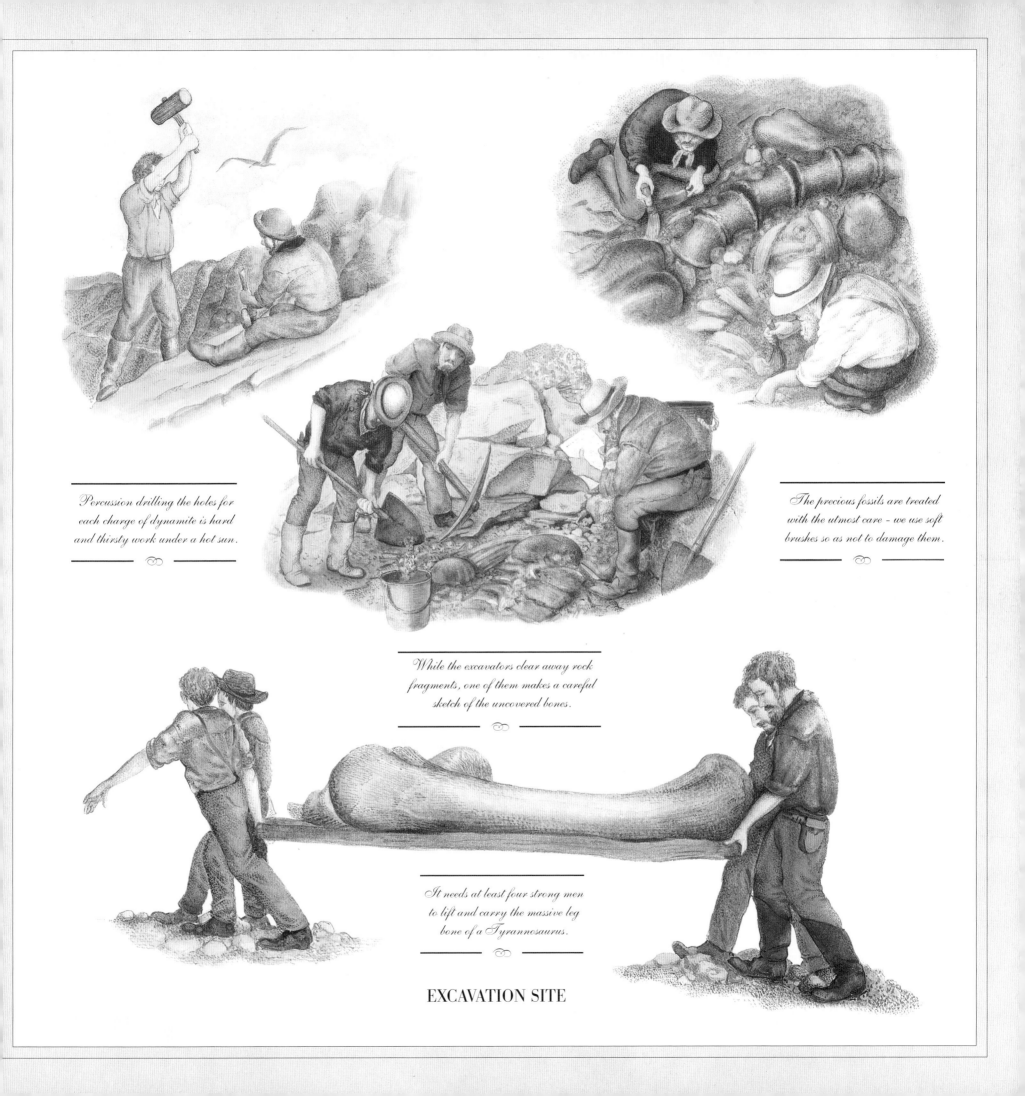

Percussion drilling the holes for each charge of dynamite is hard and thirsty work under a hot sun.

The precious fossils are treated with the utmost care - we use soft brushes so as not to damage them.

While the excavators clear away rock fragments, one of them makes a careful sketch of the uncovered bones.

It needs at least four strong men to lift and carry the massive leg bone of a Tyrannosaurus.

EXCAVATION SITE

CHAPTER III.

THE MIGHTY TYRANNOSAURUS

IN WHICH A MAGNIFICENT SPECIMEN IS RECONSTRUCTED ACCORDING TO THE ESTABLISHED VIEW

I do not recall exactly when I decided not to go back. My life as a military veterinarian seemed very dull and distant compared to my enthusiasm for fossil dinosaurs. When Barnum Brown and his party packed up for the season on September 11th, I stayed put. When the snows came, I moved to an abandoned cabin. During the winter days I spent many cold hours measuring and sketching Tyrannosaurus *bones. In the evenings, when warmed beside a log fire, I would close my eyes and imagine how the great beast had looked when those long-dead bones were covered with living flesh.*

DEADLY GIANT

Tyrannosaurus is the largest carnivorous dinosaur yet to be discovered. It stood more than 20 feet tall, measured twice that distance from snout to tail, and must have weighed something like ten tons.* The skull is massive, measuring more than 70 inches from front to back. The eyes are situated so as to face forwards, as might be expected in a hunter that has to concentrate on its prey. The jaws are hinged so they could open wide to deliver a killing bite with rows of long, sharp teeth. The neck is strong and flexible, as is the whole of the spine. The beast walked on its hind limbs, which had thick bones that show signs of being attached to powerful muscles. The feet had three toes, each tipped with a curved claw. The tail was long and heavy.

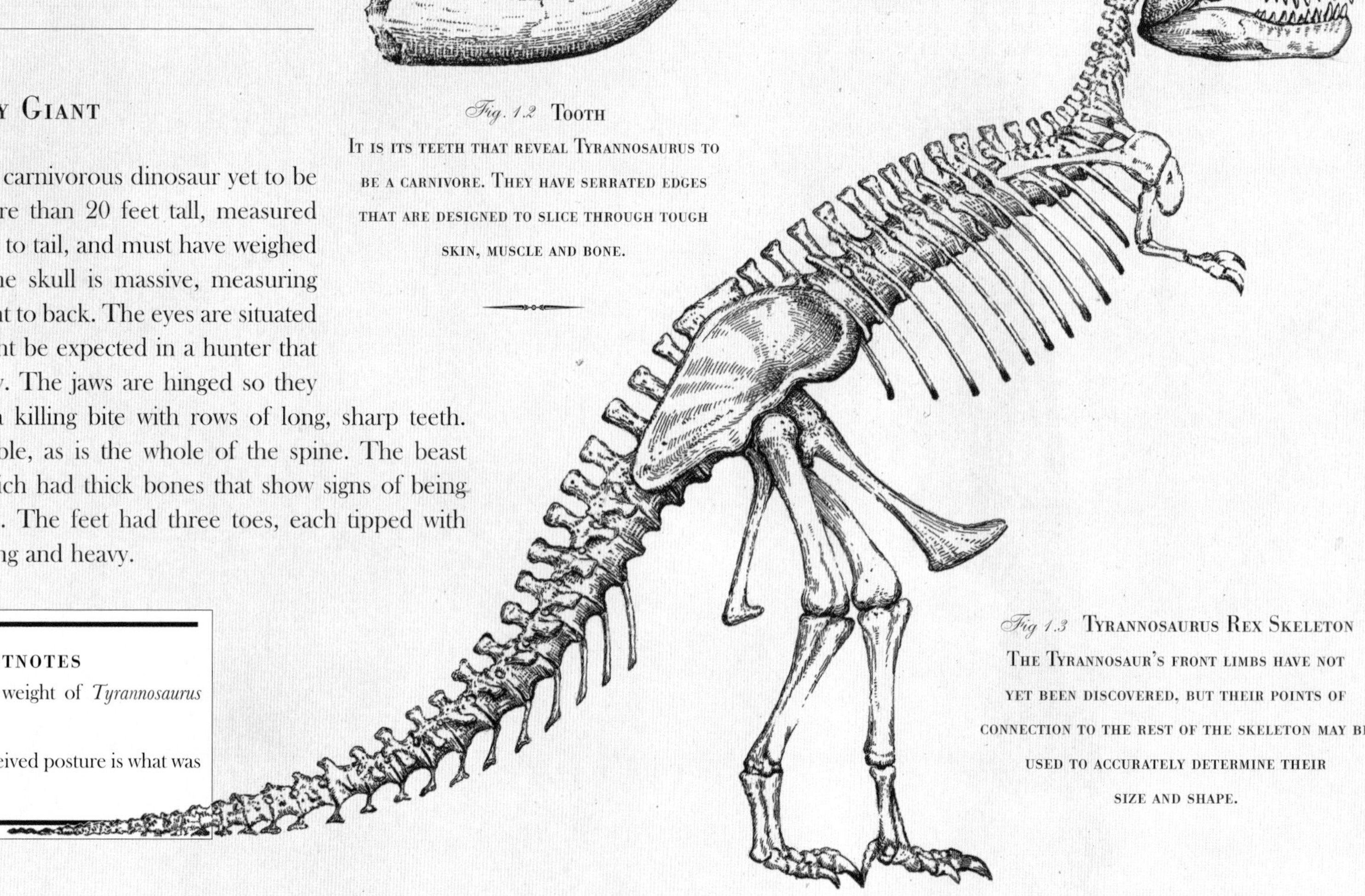

---

* EDITOR'S FOOTNOTES

* Modern scientists estimate the weight of *Tyrannosaurus* at about 6 tons.

** Monty's description of the perceived posture is what was believed at the time.

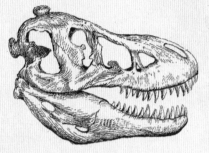

Fig. 1.1 SKULL
THE SIZE AND SHAPE OF THE OPENINGS IN THE SKULL ARE COMPELLING EVIDENCE FOR THE REPTILIAN NATURE OF DINOSAURS.

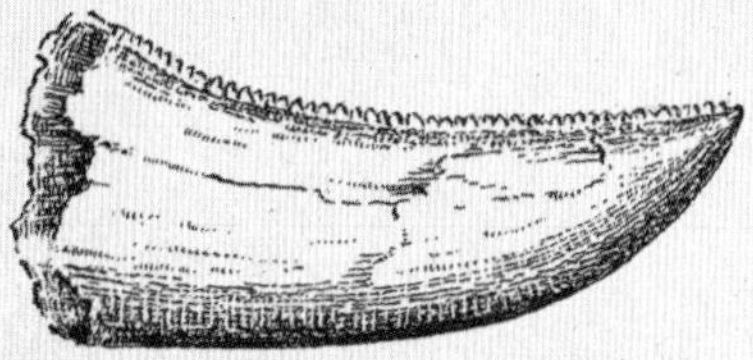

Fig. 1.2 TOOTH
IT IS ITS TEETH THAT REVEAL TYRANNOSAURUS TO BE A CARNIVORE. THEY HAVE SERRATED EDGES THAT ARE DESIGNED TO SLICE THROUGH TOUGH SKIN, MUSCLE AND BONE.

A KANGAROO STANCE?

According to expert opinion, *Tyrannosaurus* had an upright posture, and this is how it is depicted in the accompanying plate (opposite). When standing, the dinosaur may have used its tail as a support, as does the Australian kangaroo. When walking, the tail of *Tyrannosaurus* probably dragged along the ground. It seems doubtful that the beast could have attained any great speed. The hind limbs were strong and powerfully muscled, but they had to support some ten tons of weight, and the animal could not have managed more than a few miles per hour.**

Fig 1.3 TYRANNOSAURUS REX SKELETON
THE TYRANNOSAUR'S FRONT LIMBS HAVE NOT YET BEEN DISCOVERED, BUT THEIR POINTS OF CONNECTION TO THE REST OF THE SKELETON MAY BE USED TO ACCURATELY DETERMINE THEIR SIZE AND SHAPE.

TYRANNOSAURUS REX

Tyrant lizard and king of the dinosaurs, this was truly the most terrible and fearsome creature that ever stalked the Earth.

CHAPTER IV.

ALLOSAURUS & CERATOSAURUS

IN WHICH TWO LARGE CARNIVORES FROM PREHISTORIC UTAH ARE COMPARED

In the very early spring of 1909 I travelled south to Utah for a few weeks. I wanted to examine the locations of certain other dinosaurs that had been discovered in the previous century.* The going was much harder than I had anticipated, and a few weeks turned into a few months. By the time I eventually returned to Montana, the museum expedition had packed up for the year and headed east. I subsequently learned that in the following year (1910) Barnum Brown decided to seek fossils farther to the north, across the border into Canada.

TOWERS OF ROCK

THIS VALLEY IN UTAH IS STREWN WITH IMMENSE ROCK PILLARS, WHICH STAND LIKE MONUMENTS TO THE GREAT AGE OF THE EARTH.

ALLOSAURUS

This fearsome reptile was a carnivore that preyed on the herds of gigantic, long-necked dinosaurs (such as *Camarasaurus*) that lumbered across the American landscape millions of years ago. *Allosaurus* was about 30 feet in length. It was three-quarters the length of a *Tyrannosaur*, but was not as strongly built – *Allosaurus* weighed about 2 tons at most. It had powerful jaws with sharp teeth, and its forelimbs were of a size sufficient to have been useful in attack or defence. *Allosaurus* bones have been found in fairly large numbers, and it is thought that this dinosaur may have hunted in groups. This is hardly surprising, considering that at 20-ton *Camarasaurus* would have provided enough meat for at least a dozen *Allosaurus*.

CERATOSAURUS

Ceratosaurus was a medium-sized, carnivorous dinosaur about 20 feet long. It must have lived at the same time as *Allosaurus* because their bones are found together in the rocks, although the *Ceratosaurus* bones are greatly outnumbered by those of its larger rival. Both of these dinosaurs had sharp, curved teeth, and walked on their hind legs, but there are many differences between them. Chiefly it is the shape of the skull that differs. A *Ceratosaurus* skull is easily recognised by its three horns – one large horn on its snout and a pair of smaller horns above its eyes. These dinosaurs were discovered in rocks that date to the Jurassic period, and are therefore millions of years older than the Cretaceous rocks of eastern Montana. There are clear similarities between the skulls of Jurassic *Allosaurus* and Cretaceous *Tyrannosaurus*. For comparison purposes I also illustrate the skull of the *Albertosaurus* (discovered in Canada in 1879), which also dates from the Cretaceous period. I perceive very clear resemblances between these three dinosaurs (two Cretaceous and one Jurassic), while horned *Ceratosaurus* would appear to be less closely related.

---

*EDITOR'S FOOTNOTE

The famous US palaeontologist Professor Othniel Marsh discovered these two dinosaurs in the late 1870s. Fitzgibbon, however, appears to have stumbled across the Cleveland-Lloyd site where thousands of dinosaur bones were discovered in the 1940s.

Fig. 2 COMPARING THE SKULLS OF CARNIVOROUS DINOSAURS

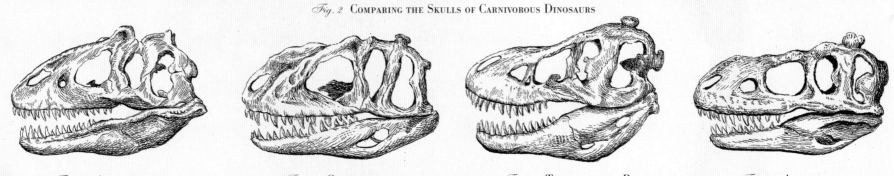

Fig. 2.1 ALLOSAURUS   *Fig. 2.2* CERATOSAURUS   *Fig. 2.3* TYRANNOSAURUS REX   *Fig. 2.4* ALBERTOSAURUS

Note that the skulls of Allosaurus, Tyrannosaurus and Albertosaurus have the same number of openings, although they differ somewhat in shape.

A FIGHT FOR THE FEAST

This hungry Ceratosaur has brought down a baby sauropod, but it will be the larger and stronger Allosaurus that dines this Jurassic day.

CHAPTER V.

THOUGHTS AND IDEAS

— ◆ —

IN WHICH AN AMATEUR DARES QUESTION THE OPINION OF EXPERTS

I confess to being somewhat surprised by the ease with which I took to a solitary, wandering life outdoors. Having spent my life in the close confines of home, university and military establishments – with regular meals and neatly made beds – I felt a deep sense of freedom. That is not to say that my life was easy. I often went hungry and occasionally found myself in serious peril. Having ventured onto higher slopes, I was engulfed by a sudden blizzard howling down from Canada. I burrowed into a nearby snow bank seeking shelter, and instead was confronted with the most grievous danger. I had unknowingly tunnelled my way into the den of a fearsome grizzly bear! Fortunately it was a male bear, which is the largest but not the fiercest of the species. Seeing that I posed no immediate threat, it chose to ignore me and I was able to make good my escape. However, had it been a female with a cub, I fear my life would have been forfeit to the fiercely protective urges of the maternal instinct.

GRIZZLY DANGER

I WAS IN TOO MUCH OF A PANIC TO GET MORE
THAN THE BRIEFEST GLIMPSE OF THE BEAR THAT
I HAD INADVERTENTLY ROUSED
FROM ITS WINTER SLUMBER.

— ◆ —

THE ILLUSTRATION OF DINOSAURS

When dinosaurs were first described, they were portrayed as walking on four legs in the manner of elephants. Further discoveries, such as that of *Tyrannosaurus*, have shown that some of them were bipedal (they walked on two legs). The experts have depicted such dinosaurs in an upright kangaroo-like posture. Perhaps it is my veterinary training – I am as familiar with some animal skeletons as I am with the living animals themselves – that makes me question this.

A NEW IDEA

My own interpretation is that these bipedal dinosaurs stood and walked with their bodies held in an almost horizontal position. Furthermore, and again contrary to expert opinion, I believe they held their tails up off the ground in order to maintain their balance. In this position, it is not impossible that *Tyrannosaurus* and other similar dinosaurs could lumber along at some considerable speed, over short distances at least. This speed of movement would greatly assist them in catching their prey.

Fig. 3 DETAILS ON THE TYRANNOSAURUS

PLANTS AND DINOSAURS

I had learned from my mentor that the plant fossils found near a dinosaur could provide a clue to the type of environment that the animal inhabited. Around the *Tyrannosaurus* fossil in Montana, I had noted mostly ferns, but also a few distinctively broad-leafed species such as sycamore. In Utah, however, I saw only ferns and the strange ginkgo, which is not a broad-leafed tree. The two localities are only a few hundred miles apart. At present they have similar climates and similar vegetation – so why was that not the case in the ancient past? The only reason I can offer the reader is that the dinosaurs in Utah lived much longer ago than *Tyrannosaurus* in Montana. Perhaps in those long distant Jurassic times there were no broad-leafed plants, and that is why there are only fern and ginkgo fossils around the Utah dinosaurs.

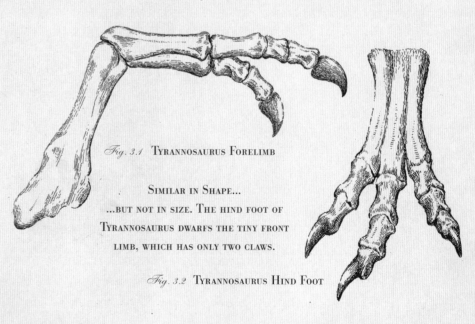

Fig. 3.1 TYRANNOSAURUS FORELIMB

SIMILAR IN SHAPE...
...BUT NOT IN SIZE. THE HIND FOOT OF
TYRANNOSAURUS DWARFS THE TINY FRONT
LIMB, WHICH HAS ONLY TWO CLAWS.

Fig. 3.2 TYRANNOSAURUS HIND FOOT

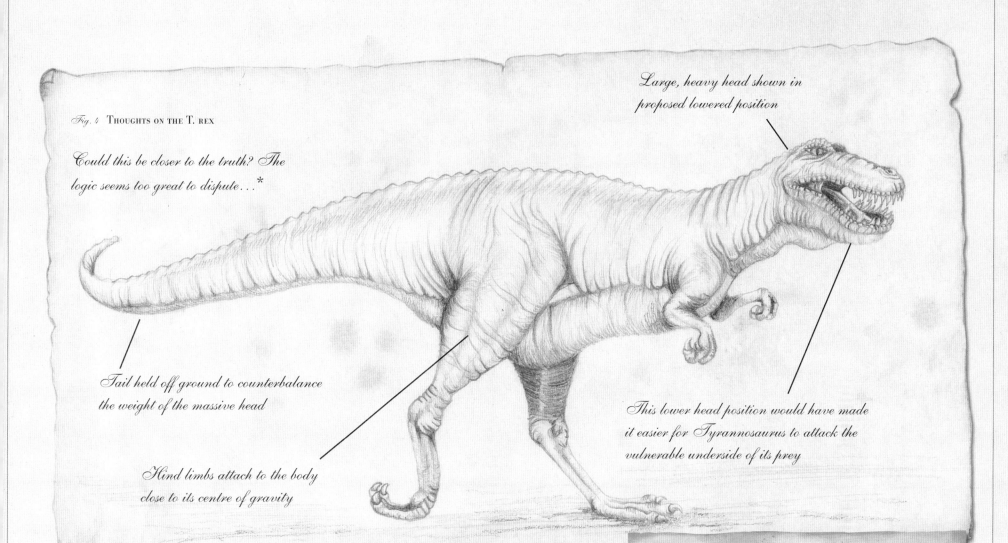

Fig. 4 THOUGHTS ON THE T. REX

Could this be closer to the truth? The logic seems too great to dispute... *

Large, heavy head shown in proposed lowered position

Tail held off ground to counterbalance the weight of the massive head

Hind limbs attach to the body close to its centre of gravity

This lower head position would have made it easier for Tyrannosaurus to attack the vulnerable underside of its prey

During one period of exceptionally cold weather, when I was forced to stay close to my campfire, I decided to test my theory about the posture of *Tyrannosaurus* by making a wooden model. Rather than carve it from one solid piece of wood, I whittled a series of flat pieces that slotted together. Needless to say, I was not surprised to find that my little model stood up extremely well, and had no need to use its tail as a kangaroo-style prop.

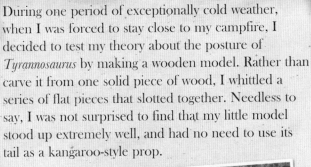

ALTERNATE VIEW

I DARE TO SUGGEST THAT TYRANNOSAURUS WAS A MORE DYNAMIC BEAST THAN IS USUALLY PORTRAYED.

PLANT LIFE

IT SEEMS LIKELY THAT AN AGE OF FERNS PRECEDED THE AGE OF BROAD-LEAVED TREES, JUST AS THE AGE OF REPTILES PRECEDED THE AGE OF MAMMALS.

Fig. 5 FOSSIL PLANTS OF THE JURASSIC AND CRETACEOUS AGE

Fig. 5.1 FERN FROM UTAH
(JURASSIC)

Fig. 5.2 BROAD-LEAF TREE FROM MONTANA
(CRETACEOUS)

*EDITOR'S FOOTNOTE

Although he has rendered the hind limbs more birdlike than is generally accepted, Monty's interpretation of the *Tyrannosaur's* natural stance is remarkably close to that of modern expert opinion.

CHAPTER VI.

ANCIENT CALAMITY

IN WHICH MYSTERIOUS BONES ARE DISCOVERED AND AN EXPLANATION IS OFFERED

In the summer of 1911, to the north of Santa Fe in New Mexico, I chanced upon a most amazing discovery. In truth I was not even looking for fossils at the time, just larking about. I had borrowed one of the newfangled motorcycles from an acquaintance in town, and taken it into the desert to see if it was as quick and agile as a horse. The machine was certainly faster, but proved to be less sure-footed on rough ground, as I discovered to my cost when I skidded down a hillside straight into a patch of dinosaur bones. Chance had worked doubly in my favour. By chance, a landslide had removed the rocks and dirt covering the fossils and, as luck would have it, I had happened upon them.

MECHANISED MONTY
PRESERVED FOR POSTERITY – THE INTREPID
EXPLORER AND HIS IRON STEED!

SUDDEN DEATH

In the small area exposed to my view there were hundreds of individual bones, and I had little doubt that the surrounding rocks held thousands more. After studying these fossils for an hour or two, I was able to make some sense of them. Instead of a disconnected jumble, I was able to discern the skeletons of about a dozen individual animals of the same species.* The skeletons were arranged as though the animals had been gathered into a pile soon after death, and thereafter remained undisturbed. There was no obvious damage or dismemberment, and it seemed likely that some kind of prehistoric calamity had overwhelmed the whole pack.

DIMINUTIVE DINOSAUR

Most of the fossil skeletons were no more than 100 inches long. The presence of two much smaller juvenile skeletons indicated that these larger specimens were indeed fully grown adults. Small fossils are not in themselves surprising – what was totally unexpected was that these dog-sized animals were undoubtedly dinosaurs. I am certain of this conclusion, no matter how ridiculous it may seem to a reader accustomed to picturing all dinosaurs as towering monsters.

I believe the rocks in which these fossils were found are of the same type as those that have preserved whole tree trunks in Arizona's famed Petrified Forest. These are generally held to be of Triassic age, millions of years before the Jurassic. Thus my double good fortune had delivered me to a double discovery – not only were these miniature New Mexican dinosaurs incredibly small, they were also incredibly ancient.

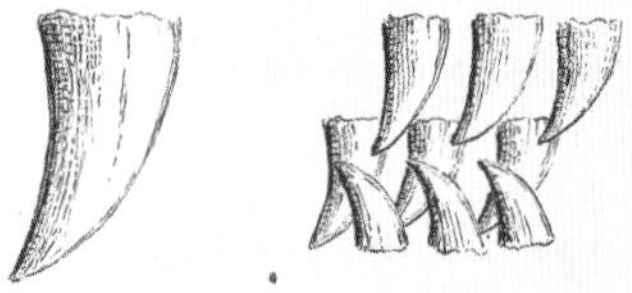

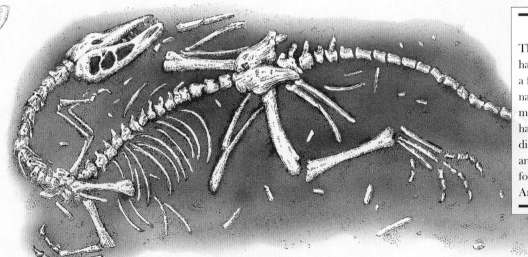

Fig. 6.1 **TEETH**
THE SHAPE OF THE TEETH OF THIS SPECIES PROCLAIMS IT TO HAVE BEEN A CARNIVORE.

Fig. 6.2 **SKELETON**
THE SHAPE OF THE SKULL CONFIRMS THAT THESE TINY, DOG-SIZED SPECIMENS WERE INDEED DINOSAURS.

Fig. 6 DETAILS ON A MINIATURE DINOSAUR

*EDITOR'S FOOTNOTE
The great fossil-hunter Edward Cope had already identified this species from a few bone fragments, and in 1889 he named it *Coelophysis*. However, it is most unlikely that Fitzgibbon would have been familiar with this obscure discovery. The fossils he describes here are almost certainly the same as those found at Ghost Ranch in 1947 by an American Museum expedition.

MANY MOUTHS TO FEED

This pack of hungry carnivores will soon strip the flesh from the bones of this unfortunate herbivorous dinosaur.

CHAPTER VII.

THE TERRIBLE CLAW

IN WHICH I ANNOUNCE THE DISCOVERY OF AN UNKNOWN DINOSAUR FROM MONTANA*

Disappointed not to meet up with Barnum Brown in the summer of 1909, I vowed not to idle away another winter. Instead I ranged far and wide across the rugged landscapes of Montana, all the time on the lookout for fossils. One cold, clear afternoon, some way to the east of my campsite, I decided to climb a nearby hill in order to get a better view of my surroundings. I never reached the top because, as I hauled myself over a ledge, I came face to face with a completely unknown dinosaur.

ROCKS REVEAL

To my delight, a rock fall had left about half a skeleton exposed to the bright sunlight. After much excited digging with my pickaxe, I was able to reveal a further portion by hauling away some broken slabs of rock. Alas, the remainder of the skeleton lay beneath layers of rock much too massive for my tools to make any impression.

MONTANA BADLANDS
THE AMERICAN TERM 'BADLANDS' IS MOST SUITABLE FOR THIS BARREN AND ALMOST IMPASSABLE LANDSCAPE.

FEARSOME FEET

The skull was large compared with the rest of its body; and the sharp teeth in the jaws confirmed that this was a predator. Like the other carnivorous dinosaurs I have examined, it obviously walked on its hind limbs. The big toe of each foot had a large sickle-shaped claw, which must have been raised off the ground while it was walking. If the beast lifted itself onto one leg, then the claw on the other foot could have been used to deadly effect with a combination kicking-swivelling-slashing motion. This sickle-claw was without doubt a fearsome weapon.

BIRDLIKE APPEARANCE

While there are some overall similarities between this sickle-clawed dinosaur and the others in this book, there are also some interesting differences. Were it not for the skull with its wickedly curved teeth, it could be imagined to be a bird rather than a reptile. I was later able to ascertain that the rock in which it lay was of Middle Cretaceous age – some millennia older than the rock that contained *Tyrannosaurus*.

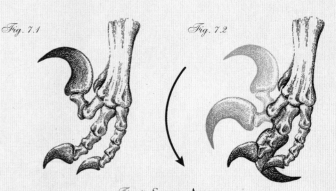

Fig. 7.1   *Fig. 7.2*

Fig. 7 SWIVEL ACTION
THE DESIGN OF THE HIND FOOT ALLOWS THE LARGEST CLAW TO SWIVEL THROUGH AN ARC OF 180 DEGREES.

MY LONELY SOJOURN WAS PLEASANTLY INTERRUPTED WHEN I ENCOUNTERED A COUPLE OF RAILROAD SURVEYORS WHO INVITED ME BACK TO THEIR CAMPSITE FOR A DELICIOUS MEAL OF PORK AND BEANS.

*EDITOR'S FOOTNOTE
We can be certain that this dinosaur is the same as *Deinonychus*, which was discovered by John Ostrom in the 1960s.

DEADLY ENCOUNTER

The tranquillity of a woodland morning is shattered by inhuman shrieks when two young specimens engage with tooth and claw.

CHAPTER VIII.

A PREHISTORIC CONNECTION

IN WHICH I ARRIVE AT A STARTLING CONCLUSION CONCERNING THE NATURE OF BIRDS AND DINOSAURS

The sickle-clawed dinosaur is a predator that preys on my mind. I do not like to think of it too much because I am led to the uncomfortable conclusion that dinosaurs and birds may be more closely related than is presently believed. I can clearly recall the lectures I attended during my first year of studying veterinary science. I was taught that birds are warm-blooded and have feathers, while dinosaurs were reptiles, and therefore cold-blooded with scaly skin. The two groups of animals would appear to be only distantly related, but my sickle-clawed discovery is not the only clue to a closer relationship.

BIRDS OR DINOSAURS?

I recall reading that around 1800 some farmers in New England's Connecticut Valley had reported numerous three-toed footprints in the rocks around their fields. At the time, these were explained as the footprints of ancient and

DINOSAUR ON DISPLAY
WHEN FIRST REVEALED TO THE PUBLIC, DINOSAURS WERE PORTRAYED WITH A FOUR-LEGGED GAIT, AN IDEA THAT IS EVEN MORE OLD-FASHIONED THAN THE 'KANGAROO' STANCE.

unknown birds – three toes being emblematic of avian species. This explanation has continued to be accepted on account of the much larger size of dinosaurs. Having now seen for myself the variation in size between dinosaurs of different species, I am led to conclude that these New England footprints were in fact made by dinosaurs, not birds.

A FOSSIL BIRD

In the 1870s a remarkable fossil was found in Germany in limestone of Jurassic age. The creature was about 24 inches long and the limestone had preserved the clear imprint of feathers that had once covered its body. It was named *Archaeopteryx* and was identified as an ancestor of the modern birds, despite the fact that its jaws contained many small, sharp teeth (no living bird has teeth). When I first saw the skeletons of the miniature dinosaur [*Coelophysis*, Ed], I was very much reminded of the *Archaeopteryx* fossil. The two creatures seemed to me to be very similar, yet one was definitely a reptile of the dinosaur variety and the other, being feathered, was obviously a bird.

Fig. 8 ARCHAEOPTERYX – THE MOST ANCIENT FOSSIL OF WHAT MAY BE CALLED A 'BIRD'.

FINDING THE SIMILARITIES

I present here comparative illustrations of three creatures: two prehistoric dinosaurs of differing size, *Tyrannosaurus* and the sickle-claw [*Deinonychus*, Ed], together with the rhea, a flightless bird similar to the ostrich that lives at the present time in South America. I invite my readers to note the many similarities between the bones and footprints of the three creatures, and then to draw their own conclusions.

Fig. 9 CHART OF COMPARATIVE SIZES

HOMO SAPIENS   TYRANNOSAURUS REX   DEINONYCHUS   RHEA

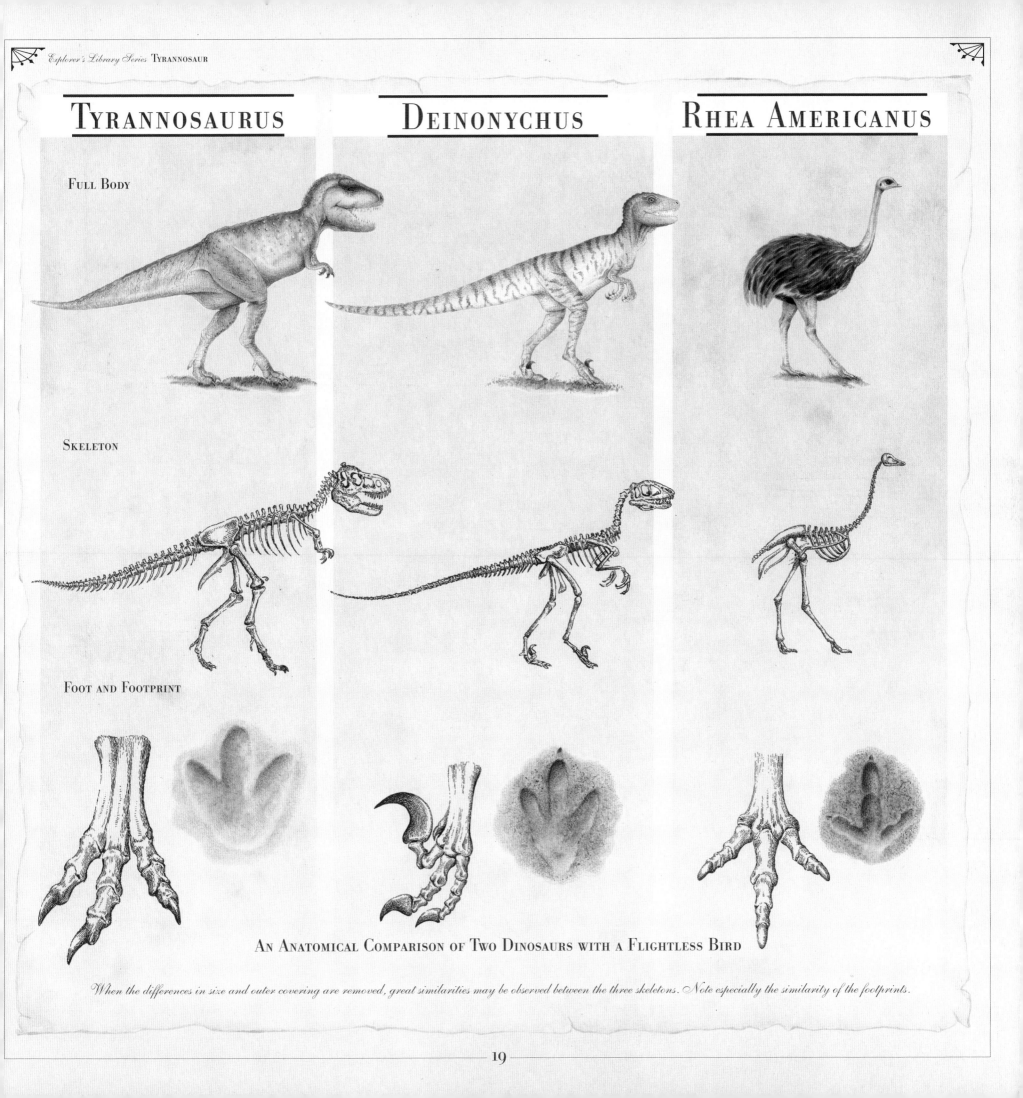

TYRANNOSAURUS

DEINONYCHUS

RHEA AMERICANUS

FULL BODY

SKELETON

FOOT AND FOOTPRINT

AN ANATOMICAL COMPARISON OF TWO DINOSAURS WITH A FLIGHTLESS BIRD

When the differences in size and outer covering are removed, great similarities may be observed between the three skeletons. Note especially the similarity of the footprints.

CHAPTER IX.

A PREDATOR IN PURSUIT

IN WHICH I UNCOVER CLUES PRESERVED IN ROCK THAT SET MY IMAGINATION AFIRE

I may have given the impression that my quest for fossils has been a largely lonely affair devoid of much human contact, but I would correct this. I had many encounters with the folks who live in the American West, and I found them to be invariably hardworking, hospitable and sympathetic to my researches. They were always helpful with regard to terrain and weather conditions, and on one memorable occasion it was they and not I who found the dinosaurs. Awakened one morning in the fall of 1912 by a sound that I had learned to recognise as an automobile horn, within a few minutes I was being bounced and jolted across the Texas prairie. A discovery had been made – one which the locals had come to know would interest me more than any other.

ANCIENT AND MODERN

IN RETROSPECT, I CONFESS THAT IN MY EXCITEMENT I SOMEWHAT EXAGGERATED THE SIZE OF THE PRESERVED PRINTS; BUT I DECIDED TO KEEP THE PICTURE BECAUSE I DO SO ENJOY THE CONTRAST BETWEEN OLD AND NEW.

SUMMONED TO THE SCENE

I was driven to a small river called the Perlooksee,* and shown a place where floodwater had washed away a section of the riverbank. Beneath a thin coating of wet mud was a flat layer of rock impressed with the tracks of prehistoric behemoths. The outlines of enormous footprints were clearly visible in the rock. Somebody had already cleared the mud from one of the prints, which was surprisingly deep. The detail of the three huge toes was as clear as if the footprint had been made only a few days previously, instead of a few millions of years ago.

---

*EDITOR'S FOOTNOTE
Fitzgibbon evidently misheard his informant. In 1951 Roland T. Bird of the American Museum of Natural History examined some similar dinosaur tracks close by the Paluxy River in Texas.

A SWIFT INSPECTION

My inspection was foreshortened by the ranger, who informed me that rain was forecast and further flooding would likely cover up the prints again. Using my hat as an improvised bucket, I cleaned out as many of the footprints as I could reach. It was late in the afternoon by the time I could make out exactly what was represented.

THE POWER OF IMAGINATION

The lengthening shadows made the footprints even more distinct – some were larger and some were smaller - but their meaning still escaped me. I had been awoken from slumber, bounced across the plains, and had then toiled for hours under a blazing sun. I ached in every muscle, and was angry and frustrated not to uncover more of the prehistoric trail. Mentally I travelled back in time to allow my imagination to see what my eyes could not – these very footprints when they were fresh. It was only then, in my mind's eye, that I could see and understand the whole scene – an ancient and timeless drama, brought to life by the power of my imagination.

I TRIED TO EXPLAIN TO THE RANGER THE DIFFERENCES BETWEEN THE TRACKS OF CARNIVOROUS AND HERBIVOROUS DINOSAURS, BUT HE SEEMED PREOCCUPIED WITH THE APPROACHING STORM.

Fig. 10 THOUGHTS ON THE FOOTPRINT TRAIL

The predator would have lowered its head so that its powerful jaws could strike at the vulnerable underside of its prey, where the skin was thinnest

Lacking sharp teeth, the herbivore may have defended itself by kicking at its attacker, or by striking a blow with its long tail

THE HUNTER AND THE HUNTED

The scene was as clear and vivid as if I had witnessed the event for myself some millions of years ago. A very large dinosaur had been making steady progress along a mud bank beside an ancient river. These were the larger prints I had excavated, and were probably made by a long-necked dinosaur such as *Camarasaurus*. The smaller prints, which intercepted the trail of the larger animal, were those of a carnivorous dinosaur – probably not *Tyrannosaurus* itself, but one of its smaller but equally hungry and fierce relatives. Without any actual bones to examine it was all just inspired guesswork, but the story in the rock seemed clear enough to me.

Thunder rolled along the flat Texas skyline as I watched the approaching storm. I closed my eyes and imagined once again that ancient drama – a huge plant-eater plodding slowly along, and completely unaware that a deadly predator is lying in ambush, just waiting for the opportunity to dash from hiding and sink its teeth into the lumbering giant.

Fig. 11 COMPARATIVE FOOTPRINTS

Fig. 11.1

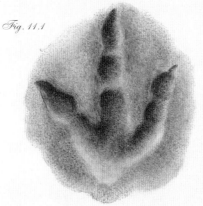

Fig. 11.2

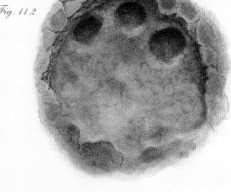

PRINT OF THE PREDATOR

THE SMALLER FOOTPRINT WAS ALMOST CERTAINLY MADE BY A MEAT-EATING DINOSAUR THAT WALKED ON ITS HIND LEGS. LONG TOES ARE A SIGN OF BIPEDAL POSTURE AND GAIT.

PRINT OF THE PREY

THE LARGER FOOTPRINT WAS MOST LIKELY MADE BY A SAUROPOD, A LONG-NECKED, PLANT-EATING DINOSAUR. ITS SHORT, ALMOST CLAWLESS TOES INDICATE A PLODDING, FOUR-FOOTED GAIT.

CHAPTER X.

A FAMILY TREE

IN WHICH CONCLUSIONS ARE DRAWN

The banded walls of a vast river-hewn canyon made a marked impression on my mind – all the more so because I soon began burning with a fever that lasted though three long hot days and shivering nights. My dreams were vivid and confused – dominated by the immensity of time represented in the layered canyon walls and streaked with visions of a shadowy beast that was half bird and half reptile. The beast whispered to me of hidden connections and conclusions that made perfect sense at the time, deep in my sleep. Once I awoke and recovered my health and stability of mind, these insights became lost in a haze of confused memory.

COLORADO RIVER CANYON

THROUGHOUT COUNTLESS CENTURIES, THE COLORADO RIVER HAS CUT STEADILY DOWNWARDS THROUGH NUMEROUS ROCK LAYERS OF DIFFERING COLOUR AND COMPOSITION.

A CONSIDERED OPINION

I have become convinced that the many similarities between certain birds and dinosaurs are more than mere coincidence. However, I am unable to further inform the reader with any degree of certainty, and I am wary of making conjectures that are too fanciful. My own opinion is that there must once have existed a creature that combined the characteristics of the two species even more closely than presently thought possible.* Viewed from a distance, this beast would have every appearance of being an ostrich or similar flightless bird. Only a close encounter would reveal that it had scaly, reptilian skin instead of feathers.

FAMILY TIES

Fossils of *Tyrannosaurus* (and its close cousin the Canadian *Albertosaurus*) have only been discovered in North America. I have seen for myself the similarities between the various carnivorous dinosaurs of North America, and I believe they are all members of the same dinosaur 'family'. This family can be separated from all the other dinosaurs, which may themselves be divided into families, although that is outside my realm of knowledge. A 'family tree' can begin with these ideas. I include here (opposite) my efforts to complete such a task, and I take pleasure adding to the lineage branches as my knowledge grows.

AN ANCIENT LINEAGE

The most ancient member of this carnivorous family – the ancestor of them all - is *Coelophysis*. Over millions of years, one branch of the family gradually increased in size, first producing *Allosaurus* during the Jurassic period, and finally *Tyrannosaurus* at the end of the Cretaceous period. Their success was undoubtedly due to their powerful jaws equipped with razor-sharp teeth. The *Ceratosaurus* that hunted alongside *Allosaurus* probably represents a side branch. Another main branch of the tree developed somewhat differently. These dinosaurs stayed fairly small, and became increasingly birdlike. *Deinonychus* from the middle of the Cretaceous period is a fairly late example of this type.**

I am painfully aware of my 'amateur' status as a fossil hunter; and that my conclusions might all too easily be dismissed as the ramblings of an incorrigible dinosaur fanatic driven mad by the desert sun. In order to address this problem I will now present this book, with all my ideas in a properly organised and academic manner, to the scientific world. My purpose in this next endeavour is twofold: firstly, to educate the general reader as to the splendour and variety of bipedal carnivorous dinosaurs in North America; and secondly, to issue this comradely challenge to my professional colleagues: if they believe my conclusions to be wrong, let them say so – and explain their reasons!

---

*EDITOR'S FOOTNOTES

NB: For the sake of clarity on this page the editors have substituted the modern names *Coelophysis* for 'the miniature dinosaur', and *Deinonychus* for 'the sickle-claw'.

* In 1914 Barnum Brown discovered a nearly complete skeleton of a dinosaur startlingly similar to an ostrich in Alberta. It was named *Struthiomimus* by Henry Fairfield Osborn, in 1917. Monty's predictions were correct.

** It is only as recently as 1996 that fossilised evidence of feathered dinosaurs has been found. A small meat-eater named *Sinosauropteryx* was discovered in China, and after more incredible discoveries, scientists now believe that many of the smaller meat-eaters such as *Deinonychus* and *Velociraptor* would have had feathers.

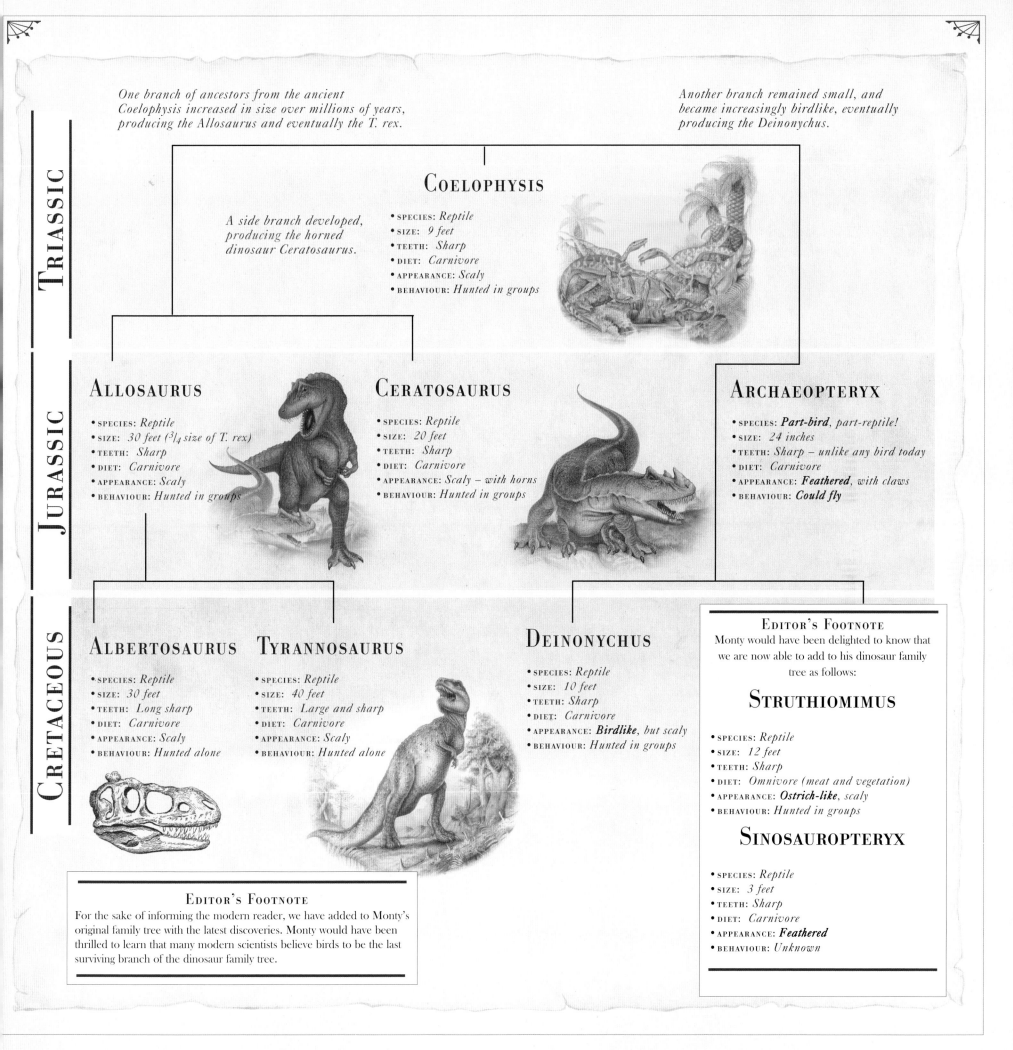

TRIASSIC

One branch of ancestors from the ancient Coelophysis increased in size over millions of years, producing the Allosaurus and eventually the T. rex.

Another branch remained small, and became increasingly birdlike, eventually producing the Deinonychus.

COELOPHYSIS

A side branch developed, producing the horned dinosaur Ceratosaurus.

- **SPECIES:** *Reptile*
- **SIZE:** *9 feet*
- **TEETH:** *Sharp*
- **DIET:** *Carnivore*
- **APPEARANCE:** *Scaly*
- **BEHAVIOUR:** *Hunted in groups*

JURASSIC

ALLOSAURUS

- **SPECIES:** *Reptile*
- **SIZE:** *30 feet ($^3/_4$ size of T. rex)*
- **TEETH:** *Sharp*
- **DIET:** *Carnivore*
- **APPEARANCE:** *Scaly*
- **BEHAVIOUR:** *Hunted in groups*

CERATOSAURUS

- **SPECIES:** *Reptile*
- **SIZE:** *20 feet*
- **TEETH:** *Sharp*
- **DIET:** *Carnivore*
- **APPEARANCE:** *Scaly – with horns*
- **BEHAVIOUR:** *Hunted in groups*

ARCHAEOPTERYX

- **SPECIES:** ***Part-bird**, part-reptile!*
- **SIZE:** *24 inches*
- **TEETH:** *Sharp – unlike any bird today*
- **DIET:** *Carnivore*
- **APPEARANCE:** ***Feathered**, with claws*
- **BEHAVIOUR:** ***Could fly***

CRETACEOUS

ALBERTOSAURUS

- **SPECIES:** *Reptile*
- **SIZE:** *30 feet*
- **TEETH:** *Long sharp*
- **DIET:** *Carnivore*
- **APPEARANCE:** *Scaly*
- **BEHAVIOUR:** *Hunted alone*

TYRANNOSAURUS

- **SPECIES:** *Reptile*
- **SIZE:** *40 feet*
- **TEETH:** *Large and sharp*
- **DIET:** *Carnivore*
- **APPEARANCE:** *Scaly*
- **BEHAVIOUR:** *Hunted alone*

DEINONYCHUS

- **SPECIES:** *Reptile*
- **SIZE:** *10 feet*
- **TEETH:** *Sharp*
- **DIET:** *Carnivore*
- **APPEARANCE:** ***Birdlike**, but scaly*
- **BEHAVIOUR:** *Hunted in groups*

EDITOR'S FOOTNOTE

For the sake of informing the modern reader, we have added to Monty's original family tree with the latest discoveries. Monty would have been thrilled to learn that many modern scientists believe birds to be the last surviving branch of the dinosaur family tree.

EDITOR'S FOOTNOTE

Monty would have been delighted to know that we are now able to add to his dinosaur family tree as follows:

STRUTHIOMIMUS

- **SPECIES:** *Reptile*
- **SIZE:** *12 feet*
- **TEETH:** *Sharp*
- **DIET:** *Omnivore (meat and vegetation)*
- **APPEARANCE:** ***Ostrich-like**, scaly*
- **BEHAVIOUR:** *Hunted in groups*

SINOSAUROPTERYX

- **SPECIES:** *Reptile*
- **SIZE:** *3 feet*
- **TEETH:** *Sharp*
- **DIET:** *Carnivore*
- **APPEARANCE:** ***Feathered***
- **BEHAVIOUR:** *Unknown*

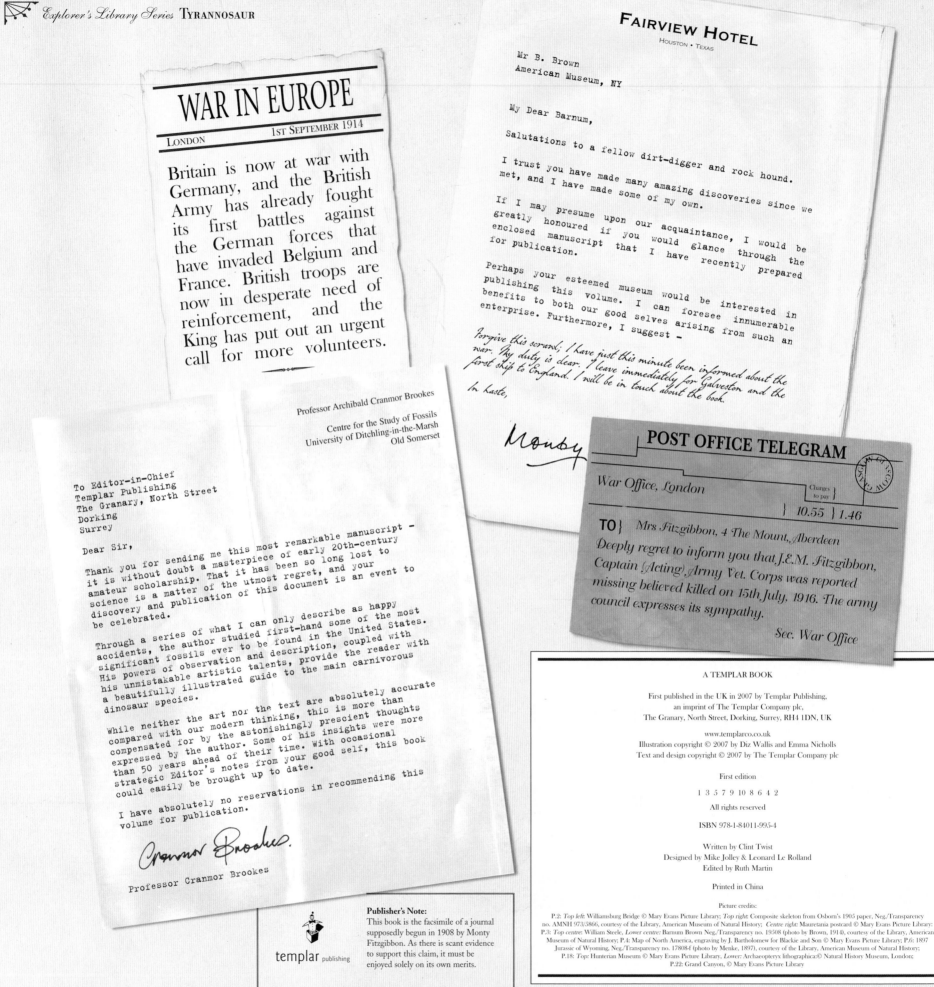

WAR IN EUROPE

LONDON   1ST SEPTEMBER 1914

Britain is now at war with Germany, and the British Army has already fought its first battles against the German forces that have invaded Belgium and France. British troops are now in desperate need of reinforcement, and the King has put out an urgent call for more volunteers.

FAIRVIEW HOTEL
HOUSTON • TEXAS

Mr B. Brown
American Museum, NY

My Dear Barnum,

Salutations to a fellow dirt-digger and rock hound.

I trust you have made many amazing discoveries since we met, and I have made some of my own.

If I may presume upon our acquaintance, I would be greatly honoured if you would glance through the enclosed manuscript that I have recently prepared for publication.

Perhaps your esteemed museum would be interested in publishing this volume. I can foresee innumerable benefits to both our good selves arising from such an enterprise. Furthermore, I suggest –

Forgive this scrawl; I have just this minute been informed about the war. My duty is clear. I leave immediately for Galveston and the first ship to England. I will be in touch about the book.

In haste,

Monty

Professor Archibald Cranmor Brookes

Centre for the Study of Fossils
University of Ditchling-in-the-Marsh
Old Somerset

To Editor-in-Chief
Templar Publishing
The Granary, North Street
Dorking
Surrey

Dear Sir,

Thank you for sending me this most remarkable manuscript – it is without doubt a masterpiece of early 20th-century amateur scholarship. That it has been so long lost to science is a matter of the utmost regret, and your discovery and publication of this document is an event to be celebrated.

Through a series of what I can only describe as happy accidents, the author studied first-hand some of the most significant fossils ever to be found in the United States. His powers of observation and description, coupled with his unmistakable artistic talents, provide the reader with a beautifully illustrated guide to the main carnivorous dinosaur species.

While neither the art nor the text are absolutely accurate compared with our modern thinking, this is more than compensated for by the astonishingly prescient thoughts expressed by the author. Some of his insights were more than 50 years ahead of their time. With occasional strategic Editor's notes from your good self, this book could easily be brought up to date.

I have absolutely no reservations in recommending this volume for publication.

Cranmor Brookes.

Professor Cranmor Brookes

POST OFFICE TELEGRAM

War Office, London | Charges to pay

} 10.55 } 1.46

TO} *Mrs Fitzgibbon, 4 The Mount, Aberdeen*

Deeply regret to inform you that J.E.M. Fitzgibbon, Captain (Acting) Army Vet. Corps was reported missing believed killed on 15th July, 1916. The army council expresses its sympathy.

Sec. War Office

Publisher's Note:
This book is the facsimile of a journal supposedly begun in 1908 by Monty Fitzgibbon. As there is scant evidence to support this claim, it must be enjoyed solely on its own merits.

templar publishing

A TEMPLAR BOOK

First published in the UK in 2007 by Templar Publishing,
an imprint of The Templar Company plc,
The Granary, North Street, Dorking, Surrey, RH4 1DN, UK

www.templarco.co.uk
Illustration copyright © 2007 by Diz Wallis and Emma Nicholls
Text and design copyright © 2007 by The Templar Company plc

First edition

1 3 5 7 9 10 8 6 4 2

All rights reserved

ISBN 978-1-84011-995-4

Written by Clint Twist
Designed by Mike Jolley & Leonard Le Rolland
Edited by Ruth Martin

Printed in China

Picture credits:
P.2: *Top left:* Williamsburg Bridge © Mary Evans Picture Library; *Top right:* Composite skeleton from Osborn's 1905 paper, Neg./Transparency no. AMNH 973/5866, courtesy of the Library, American Museum of Natural History; *Centre right:* Mauretania postcard © Mary Evans Picture Library; P.3: *Top centre:* William Steele, *Lower centre:* Barnum Brown Neg./Transparency no. 19508 (photo by Brown, 1914), courtesy of the Library, American Museum of Natural History; P.4: Map of North America, engraving by J. Bartholomew for Blackie and Son © Mary Evans Picture Library; P.6: 1897 Jurassic of Wyoming, Neg./Transparency no. 17804f (photo by Menke, 1897), courtesy of the Library, American Museum of Natural History; P.18: *Top:* Hunterian Museum © Mary Evans Picture Library; *Lower:* Archaeopteryx lithographica:© Natural History Museum, London; P.22: Grand Canyon, © Mary Evans Picture Library